Contents

*C = copper; B = bronze; S = silver; ( ) = the line must be played but cannot be assessed for a Medal.

Chinese Lanterns

Nigel Scaife

Precious Metal

James Rae

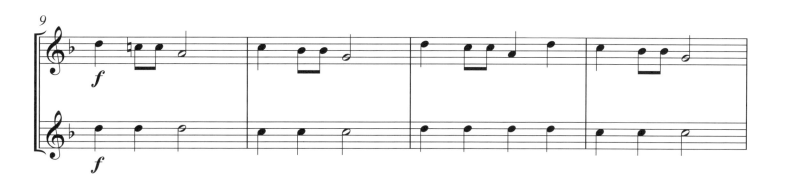

The Train Set

Robert Tucker

AB 3021

In the Mode

Cecilia McDowall

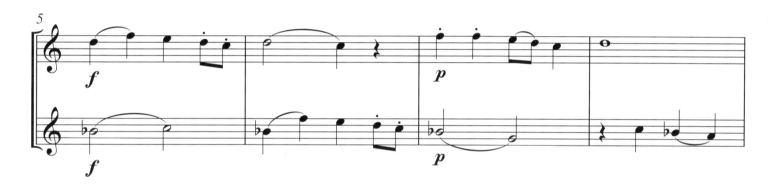

Anyone for Tennis?

Paul Harris

AB 3021

Break Time

Sarah Watts

AB 3021

7

You've Been Tangoed

Mark Goddard

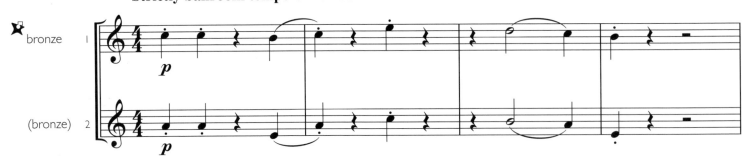

　　　　　AB 3021

Chopped Sticks

arr. Alan Haughton

Mozart's Coming to Tea

Paul Harris

AB 3021

Nice 'n' Cool!

Robert Tucker

AB 3021

The Cloudy Mountain

Sally Adams

AB 3021

Shepherd's Song

Kit Turnbull

Invincible March

James Rae

AB 3021

Blue Train

Sarah Watts

AB 3021

A Funfair Fanfare

Colin Cowles

Voyage to Mars

Mark Goddard

AB 3021

Horror Movie

Paul Harris

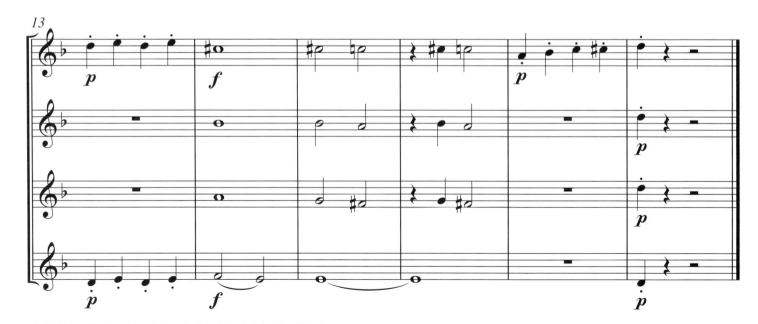

AB 3021